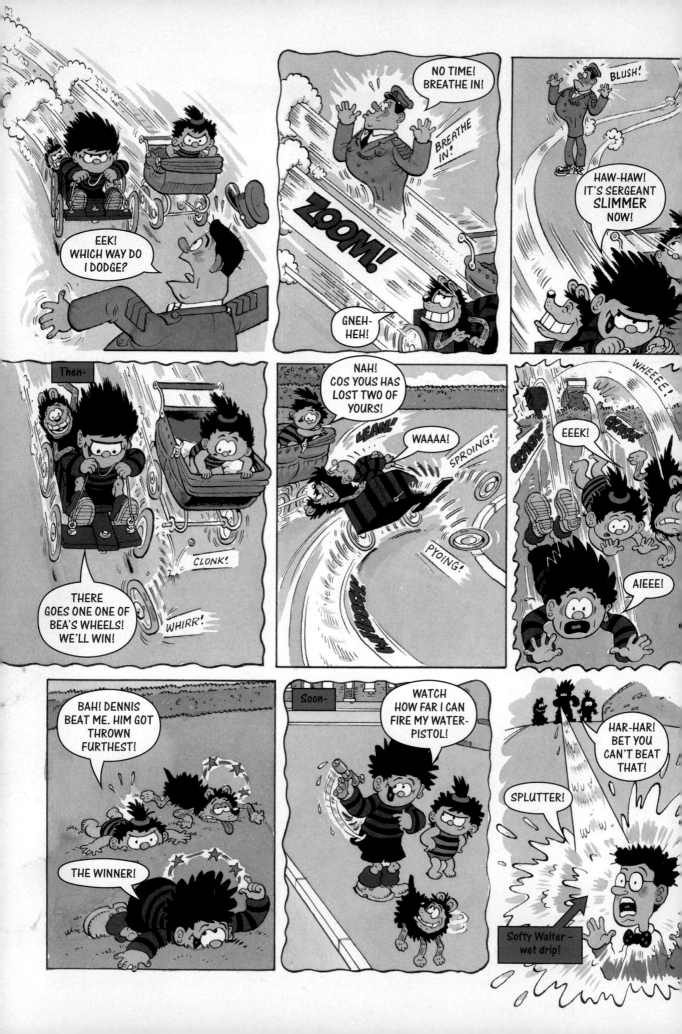

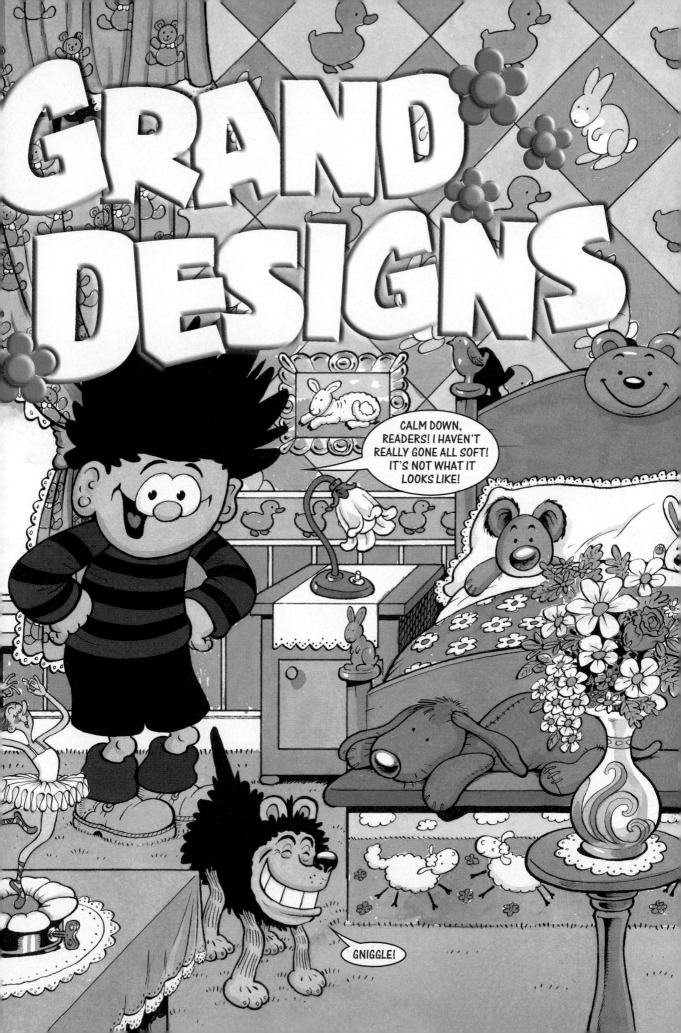

MY FAVOURITE THINGS

BY GNASHER

Draintops on noses and scaring soft kittens, Sharp stinging nettles and posties well bitten.

Big fat pork sausages in a long string – These are a few of my favourite things!

Cream covered bonies and dog food pot noodles, Hair gel and mince smells and gnashing Walt's poodle.

Wild geese that fight with swing of their wings – These a few of my favourite thin

Boys in white shell suits with blue satin sashes, Jumping in puddles and making big splashes.
Gnashing in Winter and gnashing in Spring – These are a few of my favourite things!
When it's bath night, When those weeds sing, When life seems a drag-
I simply remember my favourite things And then my tail starts to wag!
D.S

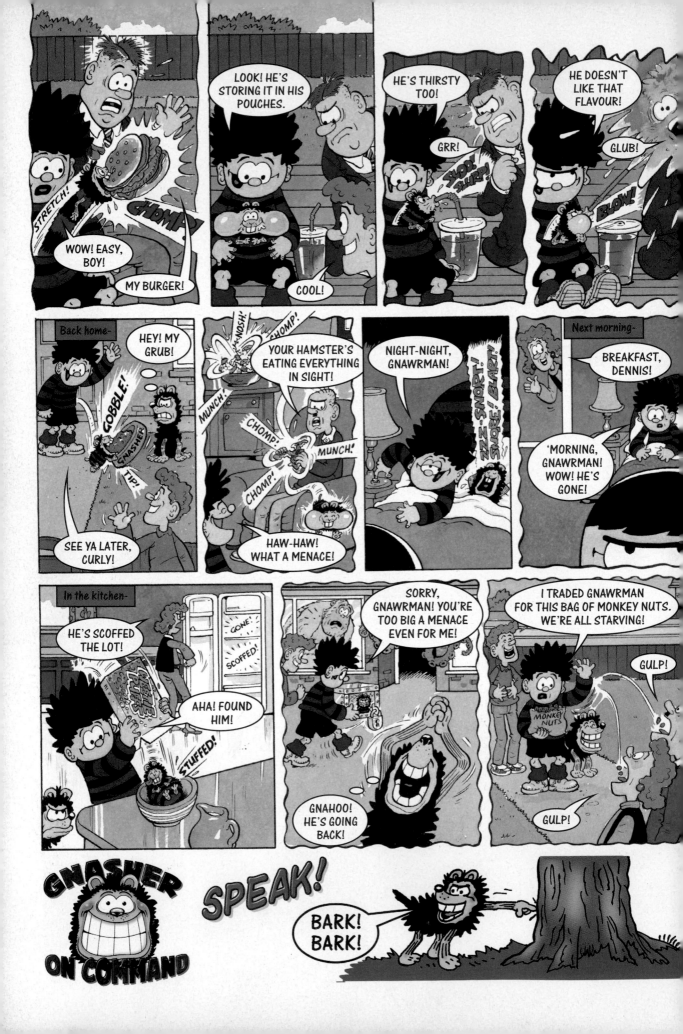

BUNGLE in the JUNGLE

AAAA-AAAA-AAAAA!

Long...long...long ago, when Beanotown was just a jungle, there lived a naughty, young native boy named Dennis. He and his faithful chimp, Gnasher, were always in trouble with the other jungle dwellers. Let us return to these far off days...

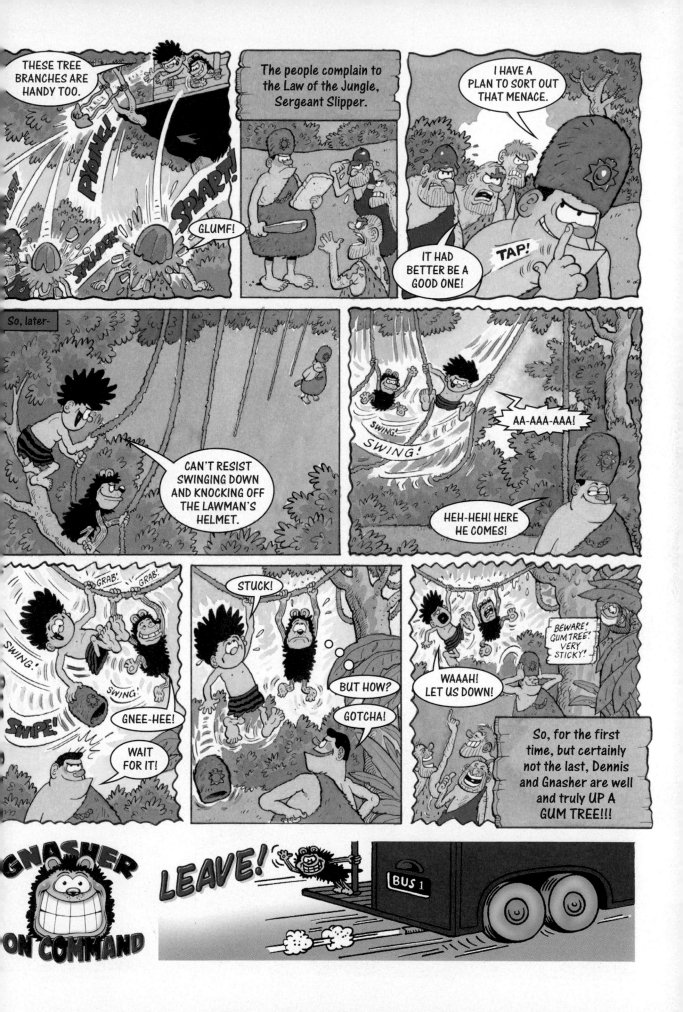

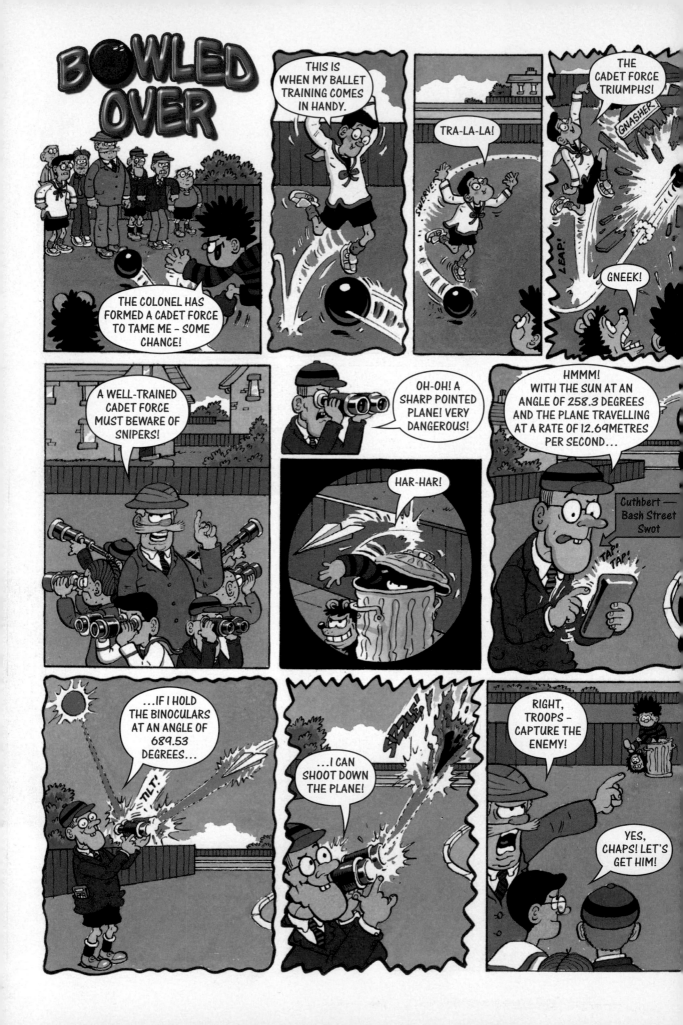

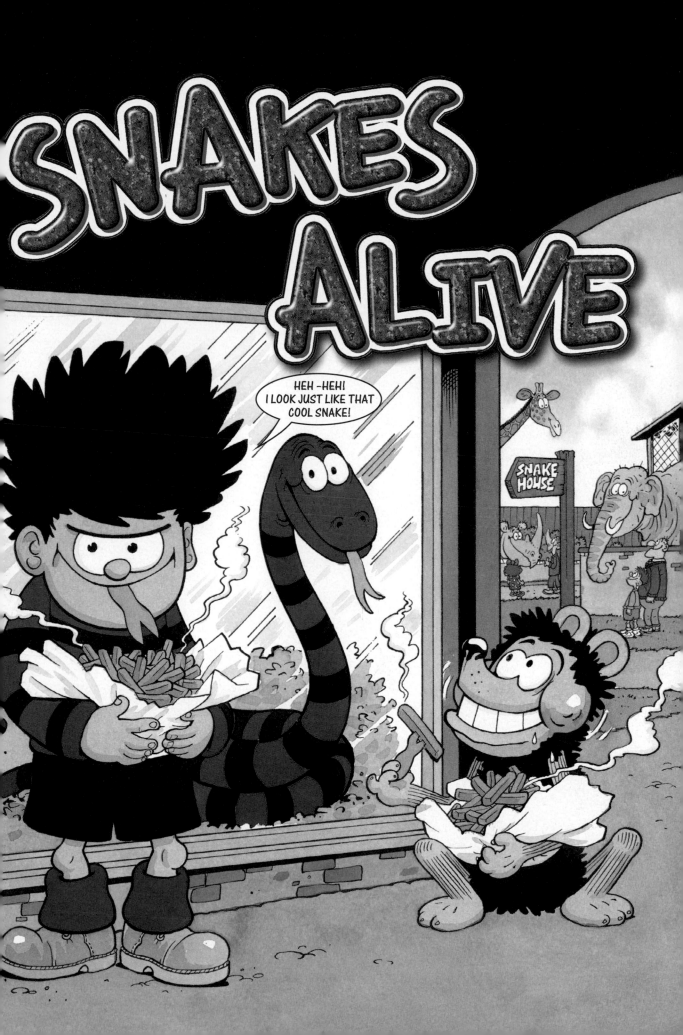

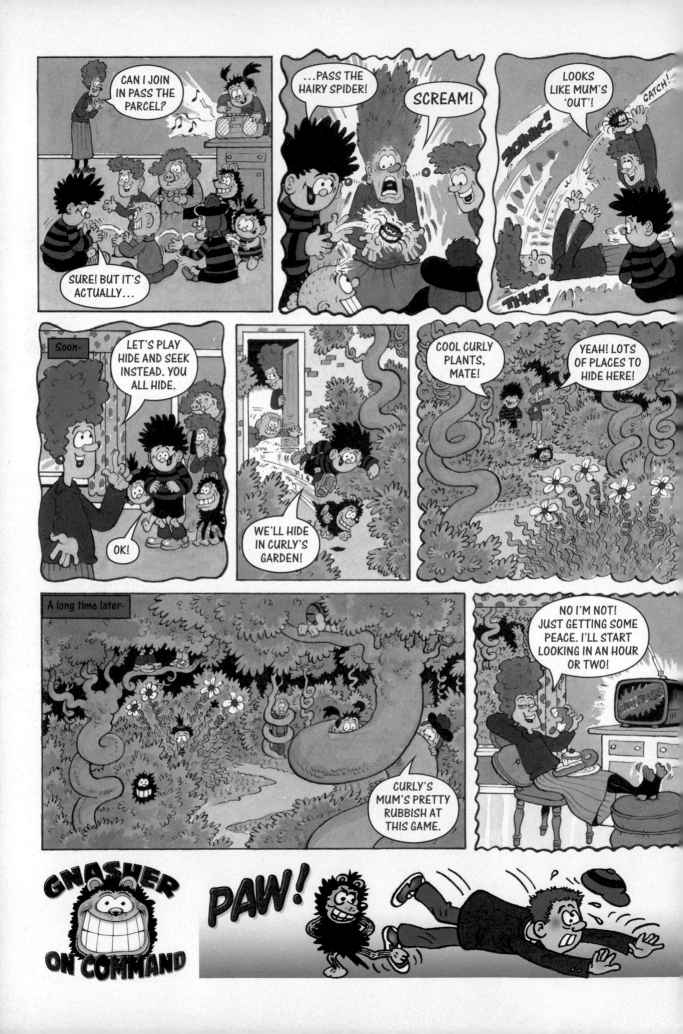

OO! OO! OO! WANNA HAVE A PARTY EVERY WEEK OF THE YEAR? THAT'S JUST WHAT IT'S LIKE WHEN YOU READ DENNIS & GNASHER'S ADVENTURES IN THE WEEKLY BEANO COMIC! THEY'RE UTTERLY BRILLIANT, HILARIOUS, FANTASTIC, WONDERFUL, MARVELLOUS, SUPERB, GLORIOUS, MAGNIFICENT, SENSATIONAL, FANTABULOUS . . .
OK, PIE-FACE! GO EASY! HERE'S THE BRIBE-ER-PRESENT I PROMISED YOU!